When Humans Roamed the Earth

When Humans Roamed the Earth

Cartoons by Chris Madden

Earthscan Publications Ltd, London

First published 1991 by
Earthscan Publications Ltd
3 Endsleigh Street, London WC1H 0DD

British Library Cataloguing in Publication Data
Madden, Chris
When Humans Roamed the Earth: Cartoons by Chris Madden
I. Title
741.5

ISBN 1 85383 108 5

Design by Mick Keates
Production by Bob Towell
Typeset by Concise Graphics
Printed and bound by Longdunn Press, Bristol

Earthscan Publications Ltd is an editorially independent
subsidiary of the International Institute for Environment
and Development (IIED; charity number 800066).

We are grateful to *Punch* magazine for permission
to reproduce the cartoons featured on pages 22 and 43,
and to *Practical Gardening* magazine for permission
to reproduce the cartoon on page 65.

ABOUT WWF

WWF (World Wide Fund for Nature) is the largest private international nature conservation organization in the world supporting over 5,000 conservation projects in over 130 countries, 200 of them in the UK alone. WWF-UK is part of a network of 23 national organizations working to protect our threatened environment. Of the funds raised in the UK, one third is used to fund WWF projects in the UK; the remainder, which is sent to WWF International in Switzerland, helps fund campaigns for tropical forests, marine conservation, protection of endangered species and habitats, Antarctica, bio-diversity and global warming.

For further information on the work of WWF write to: WWF-UK, Panda House, Weyside Park, Godalming, Surrey GU7 1XR.

Cartoonists are a rare breed, sometimes they say more on one page than a writer on 20, the times I've seen a cartoon and said I wish I'd 'said' that. I myself dabble in cartoons that on reflection left something to be desired. I drew an empty frame with a talks bubble saying 'he's forgotten to draw us', or a notice saying 'this way to here', and one of a man with only one arm and one leg with a savage dog on a chain, he says to a friend 'He cost me an arm and a leg', so to Chris Madden his CV claims politically he is leftist caused I think by he being incarcerated for eight years in Bradford. However his cartoons are dead centre in his awareness of conditions of this fragile planet, his work makes you do that rare thing. THINK.

SPIKE MILLIGAN
June 1991

Peter Rabbit's last adventure

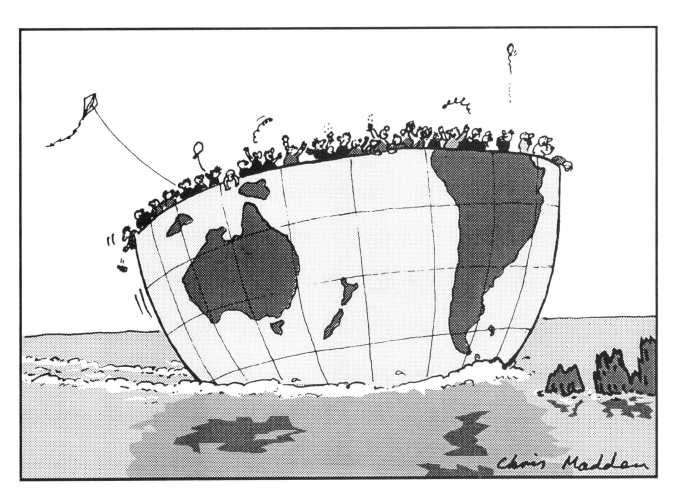

The Ship of Fools and the Rocks of Short-term
Economic Planning

Earth receives its first evidence of extraterrestrial life

An elephant never forgets

HERE, IN THIS REMOTE CORNER OF THE RAINFOREST, LIVE THE LAST OF THE SHY AND ELUSIVE **BUSH-TAILED MOWBATS**

- PUSHED TO THE EDGE OF EXTINCTION BY THE ARRIVAL OF LOGGERS AND CATTLE RANCHERS, THEY ARE NOW THREATENED BY A NEW INFLUX OF PEOPLE SEEKING A LIVING FROM THE FOREST.

"Calling flagship, calling flagship . . . the brain-impulse scanner is
picking up strong thought-waves from intelligent life-forms
directly below us . . . we're going down to investigate . . ."

THE TRAIN
THE ECOLOGICAL ALTERNATIVE ...

Their intelligence always underestimated by the humans, the woodlice eventually manoeuvred their robot into the position of managing director of Pesto-Kill

JACK AND THE BEAN STALK

MARKET

HEY, MUM - I JUST SOLD THE COW TO THE MAN FROM "AGRI-CHEM" - FOR THIS HIGH YIELD BEAN SEED!

IT'S A BARGAIN, MUM! THIS ONE SEED WILL PRODUCE ENOUGH BEANS TO PAY FOR A WHOLE HERD OF COWS!

BEAN — PRICE 1 COW — NEW BRILLIANT MODERN HYBRID — HIGH YIELD SPECIAL — AGRI-CHEM

...BUT IT'S A **DELICATE HYBRID**, AND NEEDS SPECIAL TREATMENT - EXTRA FERTILIZER AND SO ON.

BEAN GRO AGRI-CHEM

...THE MAN FROM "AGRI-CHEM" IS GOING TO SUPPLY IT.
IT'S VERY EXPENSIVE...

TO PAY FOR IT I OWE HIM A HERD OF COWS!

"Still alive, still alive – ten thousand light years
adrift in space . . . and we're still alive!"

VIEWS OF TODAY'S LONDON

NELSON'S COLUMN

ST PAUL'S CATHEDRAL

Why the dinosaurs died out

"Hey! You've got 'Small is Beautiful'
with the pre-ecoboom cover!"

The Tree of Life

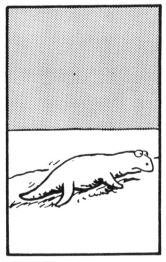

The Tree of Knowledge discovers what books are made from

Experiments in Genetic Engineering No. 1
The rabbit-proof lettuce

ECO-SENSITIVE CUTLERY PRODUCTION:

COLLECTING THE TEASPOONS THAT SPONTANEOUSLY MATERIALISE WHEN YOU EMPTY THE WASHING-UP BOWL.

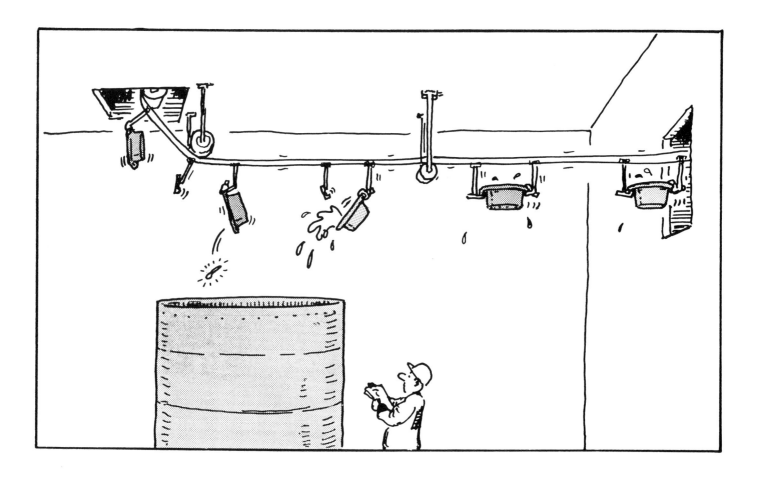

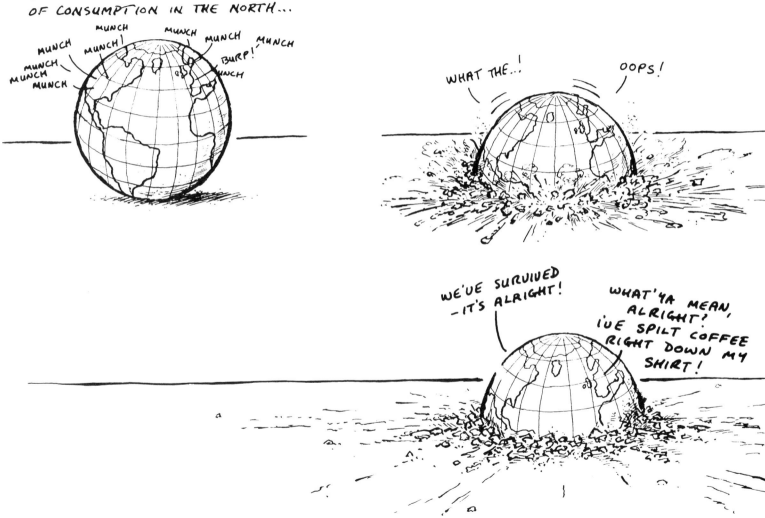

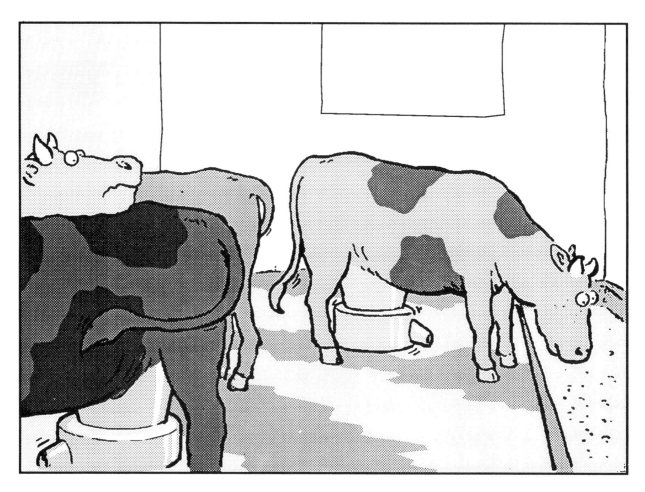

The Geneti-cow meat company's "Quik Burger" breed –
half cow, half mincing machine

The Four Truckdrivers of the Apocalypse

A coup in heaven

"Let's choose a brown one – it'll look
recycled"

Gardening Tips No. 3
Heating the greenhouse by pumping hot air up from the tropics

"All this devastation and destruction, and you armed to the teeth to defend yourself!
What sort of monster do you share your planet with?"

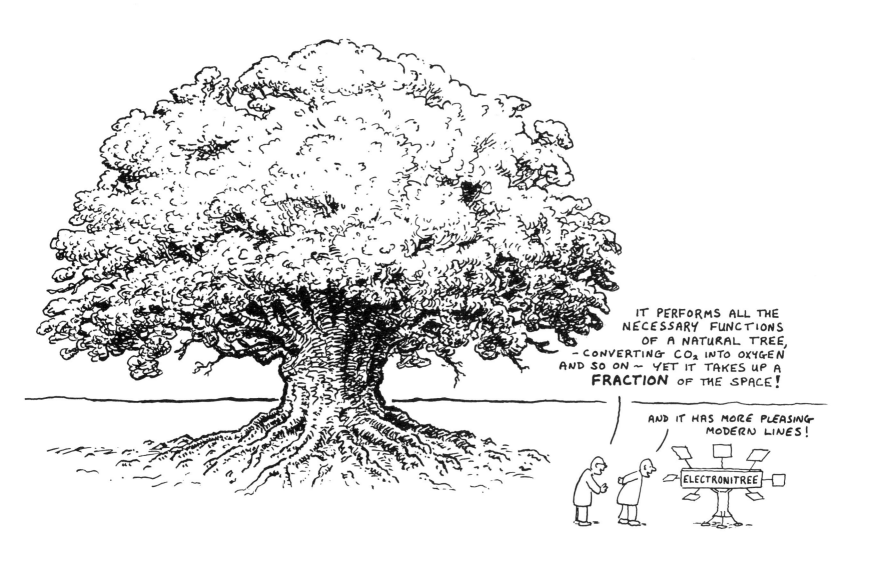

Why the mammoth died out

Eric the Red discovers America and decides not to stay

Representing the insects, the stag beetle signed the treaty
on human–animal co-operation. The humans later reneged

The End of the World